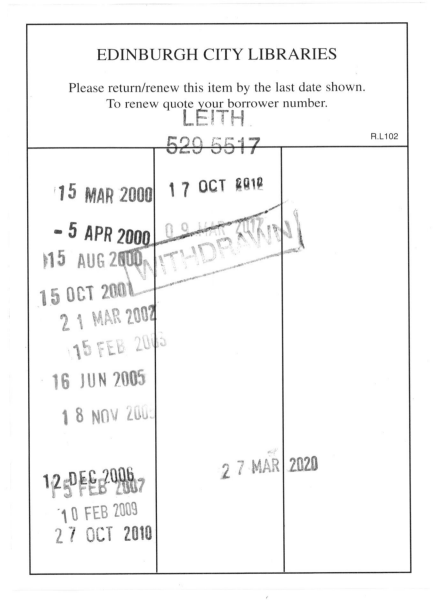

Ancient Rome

In ancient Rome, about 2,000 years ago, most people lived together in apartments like these.

Poor and rich

Poor people lived at the top. Their rooms were dingy.

Rich people lived on the middle level. Their homes were bigger and more comfortable.

We live on the top floor.

I live on the middle floor.

There are shops at ground level.

A wine seller

People collect water here, to take home.

No toilets

There were no toilets in the apartments. People shared a big toilet room at the bottom of the building.

Fire

The building was made of wood. It caught fire easily. Fire fighters had to put out the blaze.

He's having a rest in the hot afternoon.

He can smell the smoke from the fire.

People sit and chat while they are in here.

Truck full of water

Here is the toilet room.

Time for a quick wash.

Water supply

None of these homes had a water supply, or drains. People carried their water upstairs. They threw the dirty water down drains in the street.

Rich people listening to music

Kitchens

Hardly any homes had a kitchen. People went out and bought cooked meals at the local inn.

Stairs up to the apartments

This lady is going to fill her water jug.

This is the local inn.

Here is a shoe shop.

Today

This house is in a very hot part of the world. Parts of it are similar to the house in ancient Egypt.

It has modern things in it too, such as air conditioning. This cools the air inside the house.

Flat roof

This electric fan makes a cool breeze.

Thick wall

Shutters keep the sun out.

Electric air conditioning helps keep people cool.

Swimming pool

Long ago

The first people didn't have houses at all. Many of them lived in gloomy caves.

Their homes didn't have windows. They didn't even have a proper front door.

Winter home

People only lived in caves when it was cold. When the weather became warmer they lived outside.

Animal skins keep the cold wind out.

Come and see inside.

These men have caught their dinner.

These people are painting pictures of the animals they hunt.

Oil lamps light the cave.

The fire is used for cooking and keeping people warm.

Thick, warm animal skins keep people snug while they sleep.

3

Ancient Egypt

Ancient Egyptians built this house 4,000 years ago.

The sun's heat bounces off the pale walls. This keeps the house cool.

Straw mats keep the sun and dust out.

Cool inside

Egypt is very hot, but this house was designed to stay cool inside.

Lift the flap to see inside our house.

It's party time and the house is full. Friends have come to join in the fun.

Bedrooms

There were bedrooms on the top floor. People could sleep on the roof, too.

The main room

The main room was very big. It had a high ceiling, too. It was always cool and comfortable in there.

Cooking

Cooking was done outdoors. The cook's fire could burn the house down if it was lit inside.

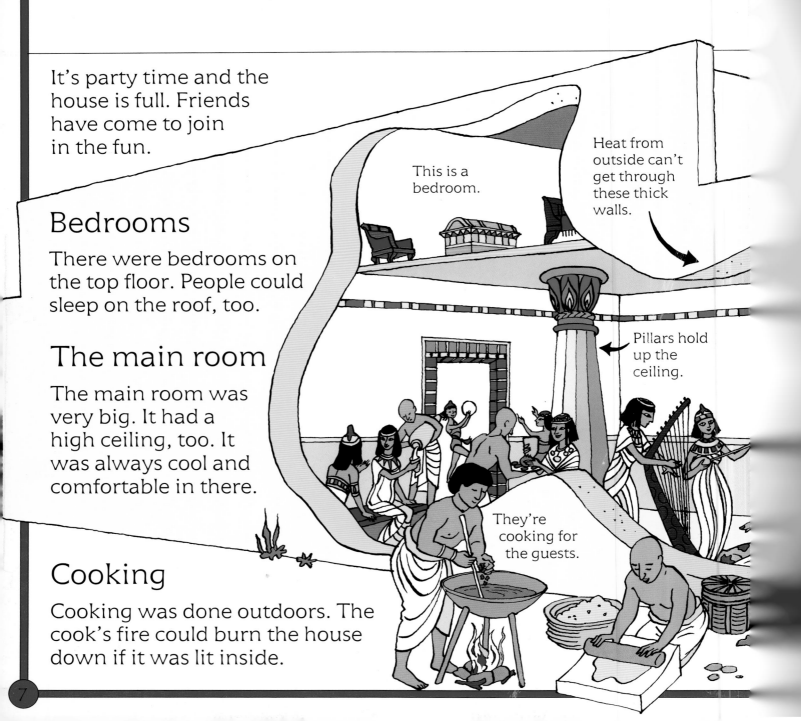

This is a bedroom.

Heat from outside can't get through these thick walls.

Pillars hold up the ceiling.

They're cooking for the guests.

Similar but different

In some ways, cave homes were like today's homes.

Cave people painted pictures straight onto their walls. We have pictures in frames.

Cave people slept in beds, like we do. But theirs were made from animal skins and grass.

Cave painting

Modern painting

Cave bed | Modern bed

They lit their home with lamps that burned animal fat. Today, most lamps use electricity.

They cooked their food over an open fire. Today, most people cook with electricity or gas.

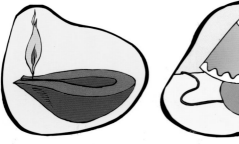
Cave lamp | Modern lamp

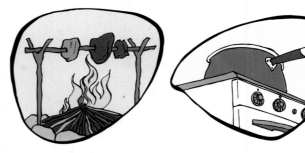
Cooking in a cave | Modern cooking

There is plenty of room in this big cave.

These people have collected vegetables to eat.

In the home

Now you can see inside the cave. Several families lived here together.

People usually lived near the entrance. This was where there was the most light and fresh air.

Not so warm

Although the cave was a good shelter, it was chilly. People had to wear lots of clothes to keep warm.

Homes and Houses
Then and Now

Written by Alastair Smith

Designed by Ruth Russell

Illustrated by Adrienne Salgado

Series editor: Judy Tatchell

In the cold

The house has no windows, so the cold can't get in.

This is a Viking house about 1,000 years ago. It was very cold during the winter. Just look at all the snow.

The chief of a Viking village lived in this house, with his family and some of his animals.

The front door is shut tight to keep out the icy wind.

Warm house

The house was made of wood. Look inside to see how the Vikings kept it warm.

Inside the house

The Vikings did as much as they could to stop heat from getting out of the home.

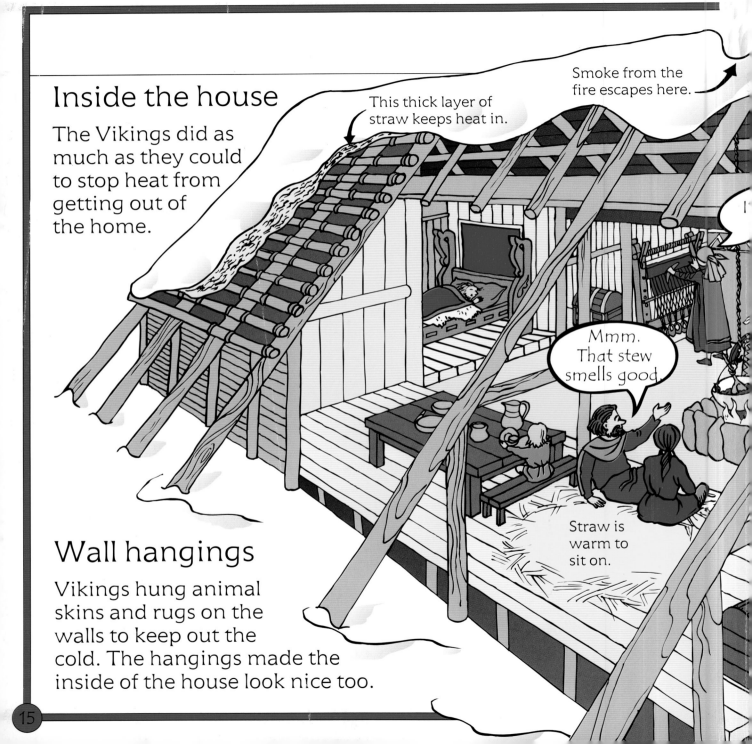

This thick layer of straw keeps heat in.

Smoke from the fire escapes here.

Mmm. That stew smells good.

Straw is warm to sit on.

Wall hangings

Vikings hung animal skins and rugs on the walls to keep out the cold. The hangings made the inside of the house look nice too.

Modern times

People still live together in modern apartments.

Today, though, apartments have water supplies. People don't have to carry their water up and down the stairs.

Drainpipes carry the dirty water away.

All of the apartments have kitchens. People can cook at home. They all have electricity, too.

The big, expensive apartments are at the top.

Drainpipe

Tra-la-laa!

It's time for lunch.

Central heating

These people had a large fire in the middle of the house. It heated their home. They cooked food on it, too.

Smoke from the fire drifted around in the house.

I'm making a rug.

This is a bear's skin.

This is the chief's dog.

Animal home

In winter, Vikings kept farm animals with them in their homes.

Inside, the animals were safe from the cold weather. Their warm bodies also helped to heat the house.

Crumbling castle

This old castle is falling down. No one has lived here for hundreds of years. At one time, though, the castle was full of people.

Who built castles?

Castles were built by rich landowners. Their huge walls and towers protected the people inside from enemies.

The castle shown here is about 700 years old.

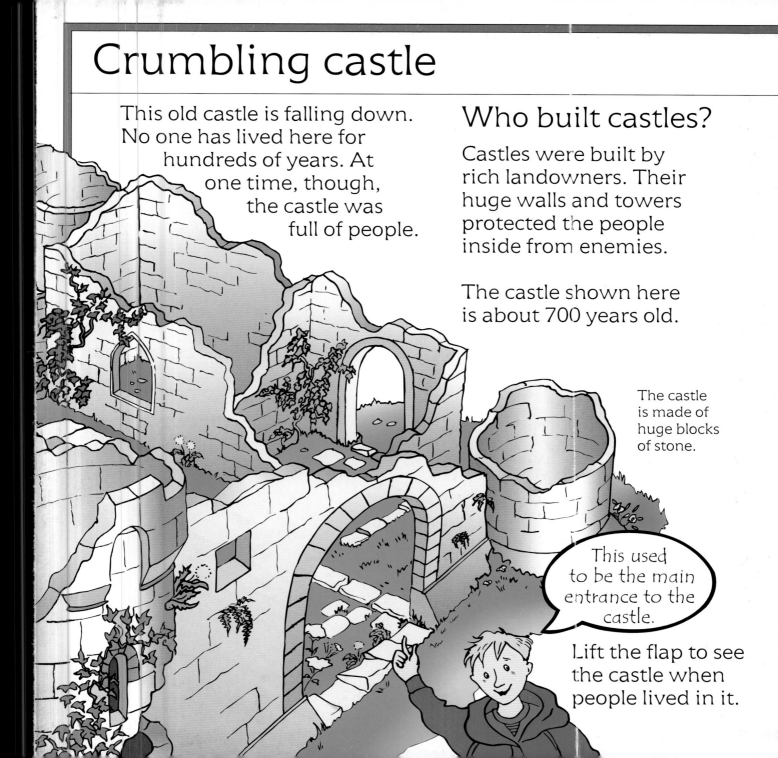

The castle is made of huge blocks of stone.

This used to be the main entrance to the castle.

Lift the flap to see the castle when people lived in it.

Defending the castle

People inside this castle are fighting off an enemy attack.

The moat

The castle was surrounded by a big ditch full of water called a moat. Enemies had to cross the moat before they could enter the castle.

Soldiers stand up here and fire arrows down on the enemy.

The walls are really high. They are very hard to climb.

19

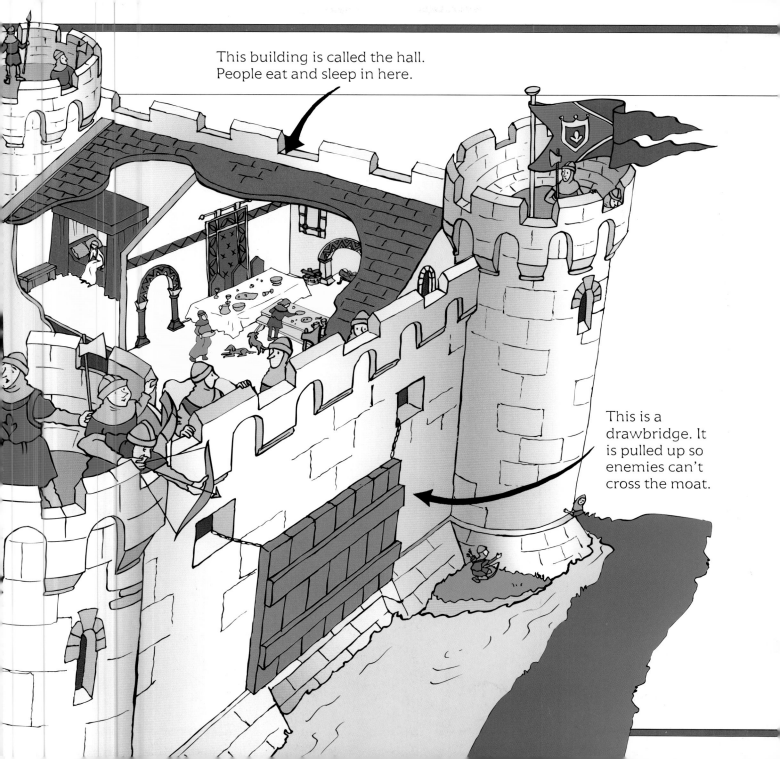

This building is called the hall.
People eat and sleep in here.

This is a
drawbridge. It
is pulled up so
enemies can't
cross the moat.

Today

Here's a modern house in the same part of the world. It is made of wood, but it looks different from the Viking house.

Heating

The house is heated by radiators on the walls.

Radiator

Windows

This house has windows. They have two layers of glass. This is called double-glazing. It stops cold from getting in.

Thick material in the roof and walls stops heat from escaping.

This stove also warms the house.

17

At night, the oxen had some food and a good rest. They stayed near the wagon.

The cover is made of strong canvas.

Farming tool

The oxen are attached to these harnesses to pull the wagon.

Food to eat on the journey

These are beds. The family sleep outside.

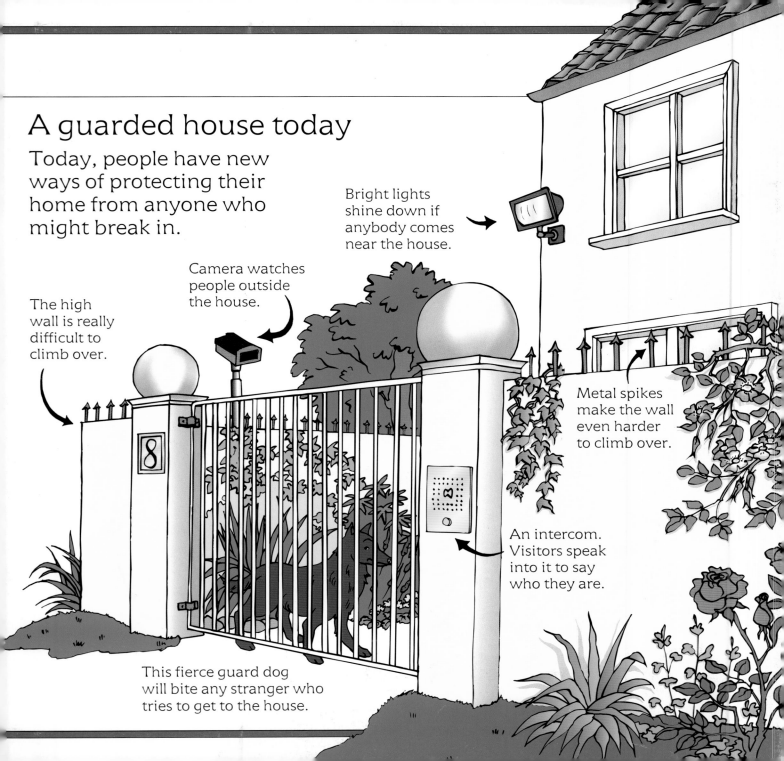

A guarded house today

Today, people have new ways of protecting their home from anyone who might break in.

Bright lights shine down if anybody comes near the house.

Camera watches people outside the house.

The high wall is really difficult to climb over.

Metal spikes make the wall even harder to climb over.

An intercom. Visitors speak into it to say who they are.

This fierce guard dog will bite any stranger who tries to get to the house.

Home on wheels

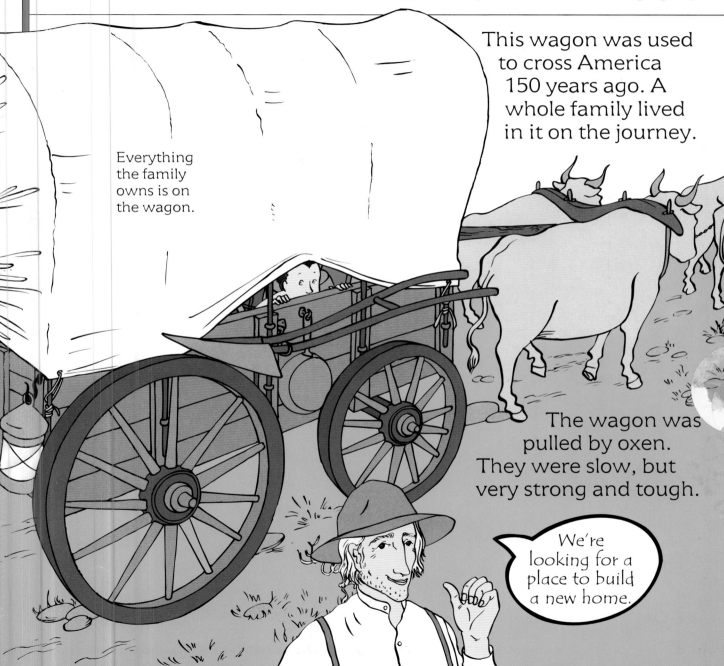

This wagon was used to cross America 150 years ago. A whole family lived in it on the journey.

Everything the family owns is on the wagon.

The wagon was pulled by oxen. They were slow, but very strong and tough.

We're looking for a place to build a new home.

Stop for the night

After a day on the move the family stopped to eat. Then they rested until the next day.

Months of moving

The family lived on the wagon for months.

There were no planes, cars or trains. It took a long time to travel across America.

This is all we own.

Lamp

Barrel of drinking water

Tonight they will eat stew.

Motor home

This modern wagon can be driven around. Most homes like this are used by people who are touring the countryside.

At night people sleep inside the motor home. They make their beds up on the long, soft seats and cushions.

Servant's bedroom

Spot the servants

Rich people had servants to make meals and keep the house clean. Servants slept in small rooms at the top of the house.

No electricity

These houses had no electricity. All of the lights burned gas or oil. Lamps hung from ceilings or walls, or stood on tables.

Decorations

For decoration, people put up wallpaper and pictures. They filled rooms with heavy furniture and big ornaments.

Compared with modern houses, the rooms in these houses look crowded and dark.

Inside view

On the inside, each house had the same number of rooms as the one next door.

Heating a home

The only way to heat a room was with a fire. Most of the rooms in the house had a fireplace.

Dirty fires

People burned coal and wood on their fires. As almost every town house had several fires, towns were very smoky places.

When the smoke mixed with fog, it made a smelly mist called smog.

Child's bedroom

I'm lighting a fire.

Town house

This house is in a town. It was built over 100 years ago. This is what it looked like when it was new.

Tall and thin

In towns, lots of houses were built tall and thin. That way, more houses could be fitted in. This house has five floors, including a basement.

Bricks and cement

The house was built of bricks held together by cement. The windows had wooden frames.

Lift the flap to see inside. You'll see inside the house next door, too.

This is the basement.

Index

With thanks to Paul Dowswell and Dr. Anne Millard.

Digital artwork by Andy Griffin.

First published in 1999 by Usborne Publishing Ltd, 83-85 Saffron Hill, London EC1N 8RT, England.
www.usborne.com

First published in America in 2000.   UE

Printed in Hong Kong, China.

Modernized

This is the same house today. Over the years changes have been made. A wall has even been knocked down to make the living room bigger.

The house has an electricity supply. What can you see that uses electricity?

Keeping warm

The house is warmed by modern central heating. The heat comes from radiators on the walls.

The fireplaces aren't needed any more. People have kept them though, because they think they look nice.

The attic is used for storage space.

Radiator

Living room

29